I CAN DO IT!

D1450456

My name is Jenn!

Written by **Laurie Wright**
Illustrated by **Ana Santos**

For my friend Jenn, who was strong, brave
and could do so many things.

Sometimes I feel like I can't do things because I'm a kid.

But I am strong, I am brave and I can do SO many things!

I feel happy when I get a new pet, but nervous too. It's a lot of work to care for animals. Can I do it?

I can prepare for the
work I'll have to do.

I can practice how
to play with a pet.

I can make sure my pet has
food and water.

I can have a pet.
I can do it!

I feel upset when I have to share my toys.
Can I do this?

I can hide all
my good stuff.

I can pretend to
fall asleep on my
toys.

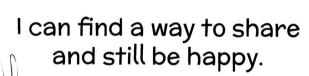

I can find a way to share
and still be happy.

I can try to share.
I can do it!

I feel frustrated when grown-ups don't let me try to do my zipper.
Can I do it myself?

I can get
dressed early.

I can practice
in secret.

I can prove that I'm
able to try it myself.

I can try to do zippers!
I can do it.

I feel embarrassed when I am learning ninjutsu because the moves don't look right.
Can I ever get better?

I can pretend to be sick and not go.

I can say that the room smells too funny!

I can practice until I feel more confident.

I can get better at this. I can do it.

I feel guilty when I do something wrong and I know that I will be in trouble.
Can I deal with it?

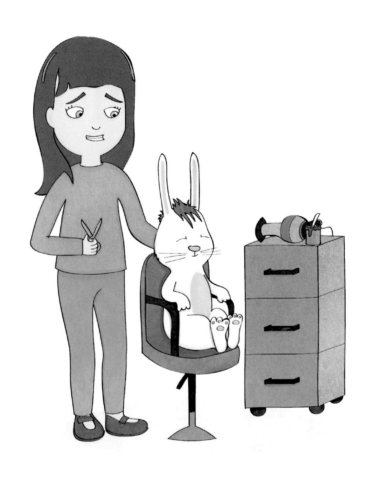

I can pretend it
wasn't me.

I can hide the
mistake.

I can make it right.

I can deal with my mistakes.
I can do it!

I feel sad when someone I love is upset with me.
What can I do?

I can pretend I
don't care.

I can get mad at
them instead.

I can try to say sorry.

I can find a way to make
things better.
I can do it!

I feel disappointed when I try SO hard but don't win.
Can I DO this?

I can stomp around
and yell.

I can see if a new
sled will help.

I can try to have fun
no matter what.

I can be a good sport.
I can do it!

I feel scared to move to a new house and I don't want to go.
I don't know if I can do this!

I can move in with a friend instead.

I can live in my treehouse forever.

I can stick with my family no matter where they go.

I can move to a new house.
I can do it!

I feel stubborn when I only want to play MY game.
What can I do?

I can try to explain
the game louder.

I can choose to
play alone.

I can take turns
playing other games.

I can be less stubborn.
I can do it!

Sometimes I feel nervous, upset, frustrated, embarrassed, guilty, sad, impatient, disappointed, scared, and stubborn,

but I am strong , I am brave and I can do so many things! I can do it!

My name is

_____

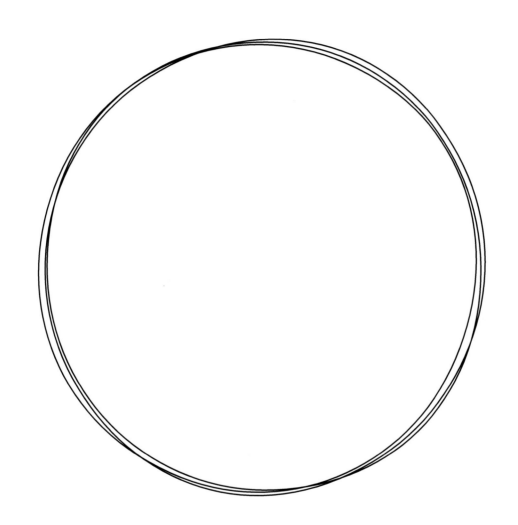

... and I can do it!

Dear Reader,

I hope that you enjoyed reading about all the different things Jenn can do! Some ideas were pretty silly, but I think it's fun to be silly sometimes, and I hope you do too.

Next time you feel upset and you worry that you can't do something, I hope you can stop and think of a few silly things you could do, and then think of a not-silly thing you could do. I know you'll come up with terrific solutions, just like Jenn.

If you liked this story and want to read more that are like it, there is a whole series of Mindful Mantra books! They are all on Amazon, just waiting for you.

You also might like a song to listen to that helps you remember that you can handle things. Ask an adult to sign up at lauriewrights.com/eight if you do.

Finally, a great big THANK YOU for reading, I sincerely hope this book has helped you.

All my best,
Laurie Wright

Laurie Wright

Laurie Wright is a speaker, author, and educator who is passionate about helping children increase their positive self-talk and improve their mental health. Laurie speaks to parents, teachers, and childcare providers, has given a TEDx talk, created resources and has written 8 books, all to further the cause of improving the self--esteem of our children. Laurie is a huge advocate for children's mental health and works every day to improve the way we interact with kids, and to help them learn to handle all of their emotions!

Ana Santos

Ana is a creative and innate illustrator and she feels very comfortable and inspired by all the challenges and areas that incorporate illustration and design. Graduated in graphic design, she dicovered her vocation for Arts as a child. Ana has already several years of experience in graphic design and illustration and she has already illustrated several edited children's books for people and publishers around the world! Ana is an artist attentive to new technologies working on many internet platforms as a freelancer.

49267018R00018

Made in the USA
Middletown, DE
19 June 2019